The Pied Piper

Retold by Paul and Gill Hamlyn

Illustrated by Helen Cann

Heinemann

Long, long ago, but not so far away,
there was a town called Hamelin.
The people of Hamelin were cross
because there were rats in the streets
and there were rats in the houses.
There were rats all over the town.

2

So the people went to see the mayor.
'We want you to do something and
we want you to do it now,' they said.
'The rats have got to go or you will
have to go.'

3

'Oh no,' said the mayor. 'Who can help us?'

Just then a man walked over to the mayor.

'I can help you,' he said. 'I can make the rats go away.'

4

The man was very tall.
He had a yellow and red coat,
a yellow and red hat,
and a yellow and red scarf.
In his hand was a pipe.

'But how can you make the rats
go away?' asked the mayor.
'When I play my pipe all the rats
will run after me,' said the man.
'I will make them jump into the river
and then they will be gone for good.'

6

'But I will only play my pipe if you
give me some money,' said the man.
'Oh, we will give you lots of money,'
said the mayor. 'Just get the rats out
of our town.'

7

So the man went out into the street.
He blew on his pipe and he looked
very happy as he played and played
and played.

8

Next the rats came
running and jumping
out of the houses.

There were

big rats,

little rats,

brown rats,

and black rats.

There were rats all over the street.

The piper danced
down to the river
playing his pipe,
and the rats went
with him.

When the piper jumped into a boat
the rats jumped into the water.
But the rats could not swim.

The people of Hamelin were
very happy because the rats had gone.
So the piper asked for his money,
but the mayor and his people just
laughed at the piper.
'We have no money for you,' they said.

11

Then the piper was very cross.
He ran back out into the street
and blew on his pipe again.
All the children of Hamelin could hear
the piper playing and they came out
of their houses, laughing and dancing.

12

The piper danced out of the town
and climbed up into the mountains.
The children climbed into the
mountains too. The people of Hamelin
called out and tried to stop them but
the children could only hear the piper.

13

The piper and the children danced off into the mountain, into a magic land.

There was just one little boy who could not walk as fast as his friends. When he got to the top of the mountain, all his friends had gone.

So the little boy went back to Hamelin
and said, 'My friends have gone to a
magic land where they can dance and
play all day.'
'Oh no!' said the mayor. 'We must find
the piper and give him his money. It's
the only way to get our children back.'

The people of Hamelin looked here and there for the piper. But they couldn't find the piper and they couldn't find their children. The people were very sad.

But the children were very happy in the magic land. They danced and played all day as the piper played his pipe.

16